READING AND WRITING FOR TODAY'S ADULTS

Voyager I

MARY DUNN SIEDOW

New Readers Press

Advisers to the Series

Mary Dunn Siedow
Linda Thistlethwaite

Reviewer

Linda Church

Voyager Introduction: Reading and Writing for Today's Adults
ISBN 978-1-56420-909-2

Printed in the United States of America
9 8 7 6 5 4 3 2

Proceeds from the sale of New Readers Press materials support professional development, training, and technical assistance programs of ProLiteracy that benefit local literacy programs in the U.S. and around the globe.

Developmental Editor: Terrie Lipke
Creative Director: Andrea Woodbury
Developer: Learning Unlimited, Oak Park, IL
Production Specialist: Maryellen Casey
Art and Design Supervisor: James P. Wallace
Illustrations: Judy Love and Drew Rose, represented by Wilkinson Studios, Inc.
Cover Design: James P. Wallace

ProLiteracy and New Readers Press are not owned or sponsored by Voyager Expanded Learning, Inc.

Contents

Alphabet

Say each letter. Write it.

A A — — — — — — — — — —   a a — — — — — — — — — —

B — — — — — — — — — — —   b — — — — — — — — — — —

C — — — — — — — — — — —   c — — — — — — — — — — —

D — — — — — — — — — — —   d — — — — — — — — — — —

E — — — — — — — — — — —   e — — — — — — — — — — —

F — — — — — — — — — — —   f — — — — — — — — — — —

G — — — — — — — — — — —   g — — — — — — — — — — —

H — — — — — — — — — — —   h — — — — — — — — — — —

I — — — — — — — — — — —   i — — — — — — — — — — —

J — — — — — — — — — — —   j — — — — — — — — — — —

K — — — — — — — — — — —   k — — — — — — — — — — —

L — — — — — — — — — — —   l — — — — — — — — — — —

M — — — — — — — — — — —   m — — — — — — — — — — —

N -----------------------   n -----------------------

O -----------------------   o -----------------------

P -----------------------   p -----------------------

Q -----------------------   q -----------------------

R -----------------------   r -----------------------

S -----------------------   s -----------------------

T -----------------------   t -----------------------

U -----------------------   u -----------------------

V -----------------------   v -----------------------

W -----------------------   w -----------------------

X -----------------------   x -----------------------

Y -----------------------   y -----------------------

Z -----------------------   z -----------------------

Bb By the Bookstore

Talk, Write, and Read

A. Talk about what you see in this picture.

B. Write words with the letter **b** like **book.** You may use words from the picture.

_____   _____   _____

_____   _____   _____

C. Pick one word from your list. Make a sentence with the word.

_____

_____

D. Read your sentence out loud.

Notes for Unit 1: 1.A. Talk about the picture with students. Use words that contain the target letter frequently. **B.** Follow the letter/sound lesson strategy in the *Teacher's Resource Guide* (TRG). **C.** Write sentences that students dictate. Have students copy them. **D.** Let students volunteer to read aloud to you or to student partners.

Words to Know

bank

book

subway

cab

Key Words

closed	is	open	Sunday	the

Read and Write

Read the sentences. Write the word that fits.

Open and Closed

✓ book
closed
is

The _____book_____ is open.

The book is _____.

The book _____ closed.

bank
is
open
The

The _____ is closed.

The bookstore is _____.

The bank _____ closed Sunday.

_____ bookstore is open Sunday.

In Your Own Words

Tell a story about the picture on page 6. Your teacher will write it for you.

Notes: 2. Ask students to read and talk about words that are pictured. **3.** Read each word; have students repeat.
4. Help students read each sentence and fill in the appropriate words. **5.** Conduct a Language Experience Approach
(LEA) activity. See the TRG for guidance. Have students keep their copies.

Dd Don's Office

Talk, Write, and Read

A. Talk about what you see in this picture.

B. Write words with the letter **d** like **door.** You may use words from the picture.

_____   _____   _____

_____   _____   _____

C. Pick two words from your list. Make a sentence with each word.

1. _____

_____

2. _____

_____

D. Read your sentences out loud.

Words to Know

desk

door

window

shade

Key Words

a	an	full	has	in	office

Read and Write

Read the sentences. Write the word that fits.

Don's Office

full
has
desk

Don's office _____ a door.

The door is closed.

Don has a _____.

The desk is _____.

a
office
window

Don's _____ has a window.

The window has _____ shade.

The _____ is closed in December.

In Your Own Words

Tell a story about the picture on page 8. Your teacher will write it for you.

Ff Frank and His Friends

Talk, Write, and Read

A. Talk about what you see in this picture.

B. Write words with the letter **f** like **food.** You may use words from the picture.

_____   _____   _____

_____   _____   _____

C. Pick two words from your list. Make a sentence with each word.

1. _____

_____

2. _____

_____

D. Read your sentences out loud.

Words to Know

fish

friends

coffee

$\frac{1}{2}$
half

Key Words

and	drink	eat	Friday	his	on

Read and Write

Read the sentences. Write the word that fits.

Frank and His Friends

coffee
fish
friends

Frank and his friends eat fast food on Friday.

Frank and his friends eat _____ on Friday.

Frank and his _____ eat french fries.

Frank and his friends drink _____.

and
food
full

Frank eats half his fish _____ french fries.

Frank is _____.

His friends eat his _____.

In Your Own Words

Tell a story about the picture on page 10. Your teacher will write it for you.

Hh Hal and His Cab

Talk, Write, and Read

A. Talk about what you see in this picture.

B. Write words with the letter **h** like **hill.** You may use words from the picture.

_____   _____   _____

_____   _____   _____

C. Pick two words from your list. Make a sentence with each word.

1. _____

_____

2. _____

_____

D. Read your sentences out loud.

Words to Know

hand

hood

hose

house

Key Words

he	hole	new	old	puts

Read and Write

Read the sentences. Write the word that fits.

Hal and His Cab

hole
hood
old

Hal has an old cab.

Hal has the _____ open.

The hose is _____.

The hose has a _____.

Hal
hand
puts

Hal has a new hose in his _____.

He _____ the new hose in the cab.

_____ closes the hood.

In Your Own Words

Tell a story about the picture on page 12. Your teacher will write it for you.

Gg & Jj   The Garden

Talk and Read

A. Talk about what you see in this picture.

B. Say words with the letter **g** like **garden,** the letter **g** like **giant,** or the letter **j** like **jacket.** Talk about the sounds that **g** and **j** make in these words.

C. Write words that have these letters.

g like **garden**	**g** like **giant**	**j** like **jacket**
_____	_____	_____
_____	_____	_____
_____	_____	_____
_____	_____	_____

Notes: 1.A. Talk about the picture as before. **B.** Explain that *g* has two common sounds (garden, giant) and that one of these (giant) is the same sound as *j*. **C.** Follow letter/sound lesson format.

G like Garden

In many words, **g** sounds like the **g** in **garden.** Read the words you wrote on page 14 that have this sound.

A. Choose two words from your list. Make a sentence using each word.

1. _____

2. _____

B. Read your sentences out loud.

Words to Know

garden

gate

wagon

dig

Key Words

grow	have	May	they	up

Read and Write

Read the sentences. Write the word that fits.

The Garden

dig
grow
They

Jan and Gus have a garden.

They _____ up the garden in May.

They _____ food in the garden.

_____ grow food for their friends.

G like Giant

In many words, **g** sounds like the **g** in **giant.** Read the words you wrote on page 14 that have this sound.

A. Choose two words from your list. Make a sentence using each word.

   1. _____

   2. _____

B. Read your sentences out loud.

J like Jacket

In most words, **j** sounds like the **j** in **jacket.** Read the words you wrote on page 14 that have this sound.

A. Choose two words from your list. Make a sentence using each word.

   1. _____

   2. _____

B. Read your sentences out loud.

In Your Own Words

Tell a story about the picture on page 14. Your teacher will write it for you.

_____

_____

_____

_____

_____

Words to Know

garage

July

jacket

vegetables

Key Words

August	can	give	them	to

Read and Write

Read the story. Write the word that fits.

Vegetables

garden
put
wagon

Jan and Gus grow vegetables in the garden.

They _____ the vegetables in a wagon.

They put the _____ in the garage.

They close the _____ gate.

can
give
vegetables

Jan and Gus _____ eat the vegetables.

They _____ them to friends in July

and August.

They give _____ to Frank and Hal.

In Your Own Words

Describe what you would do if a friend gave you some vegetables. Your teacher
will write it for you.

Review Bb, Dd, Ff, Hh, Gg & Jj

Words to Review

Fill in the missing letter of each word. Then read the words out loud.

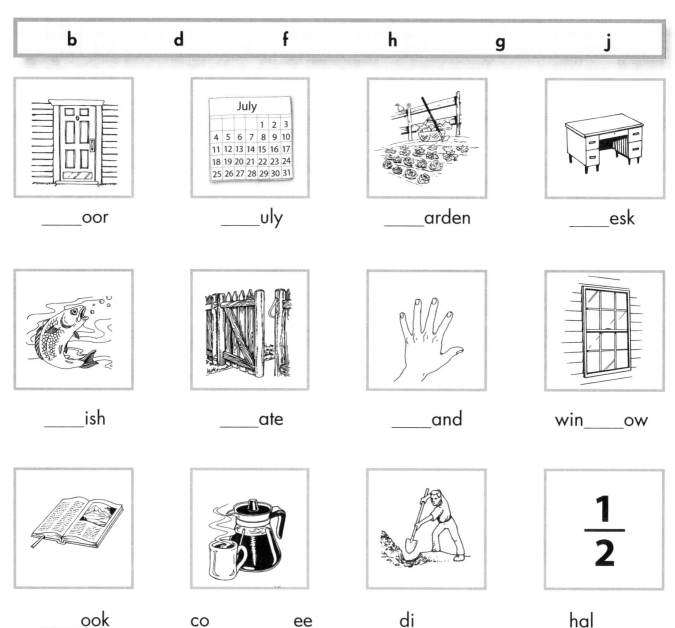

| b | d | f | h | g | j |

____oor

____uly

____arden

____esk

____ish

____ate

____and

win____ow

____ook

co____ ____ee

di____

hal____

Notes: 1. Have students read the six consonants. Help them write the correct consonant in the first few words. Let them complete the exercise as independently as possible.

18   Unit 1 **Review**

Sentence Pairs

Finish the sentence pairs with the word that fits. Read the sentences out loud.

coffee
December
hose
vegetables

A. Don's office has a window.

The window is closed in _____.

B. Frank and his friends eat food.

They drink _____.

C. Jan and Gus have a garden.

They grow _____ in the garden.

D. Hal has an old hose in his cab.

He puts in a new _____.

How Do You Know?

Check the sentence that tells how you know.

A. How do you know Don is in his office?

_____ (1) His window is closed.

_____ (2) His door is open.

B. How do you know Frank eats french fries?

_____ (1) He has french fries in his hand.

_____ (2) His friends eat french fries.

C. How do you know Jan and Gus have a garden?

_____ (1) They grow vegetables.

_____ (2) They eat vegetables.

D. How do you know Hal has an old hose in his cab?

_____ (1) He puts the cab in the garage.

_____ (2) The hose has a hole.

Notes: 2. Have students read the sentences as independently as possible and choose the word to finish each sentence. Have them read completed sentences aloud, either individually or as a group. **3.** Help students read the "How Do You Know?" questions; let them choose the more logical answer.

What's the Order?

A. Number the sentences in order. The first one is started for you.

1. __1__ Hal has an old hose in his cab.

   ____ Hal puts in a new hose.

   ____ Hal opens the hood.

2. ____ Jan and Gus dig up the vegetables.

   ____ Vegetables grow in the garden.

   ____ Jan and Gus give vegetables to friends.

B. Read the sentences in order out loud.

Writing Sentences

Make a sentence. Use all the words. Then read your sentences to someone.

door	bank	open

A. _The door to the bank is open._

eat	fish	July

B. _____

close	door	cab

C. _____

give	book	friend

D. _____

Notes: 4. Discuss the meaning of sequence. Help students put the first group in sequence. Have them do the second group on their own. **5.** Point out that the example is a sentence using all of the given words. Have students dictate sentences for B–D. Let them copy their sentences and read them aloud.

Puzzle

Read the words out loud. Write words where they fit. Use all the words. Some letters are there to help you.

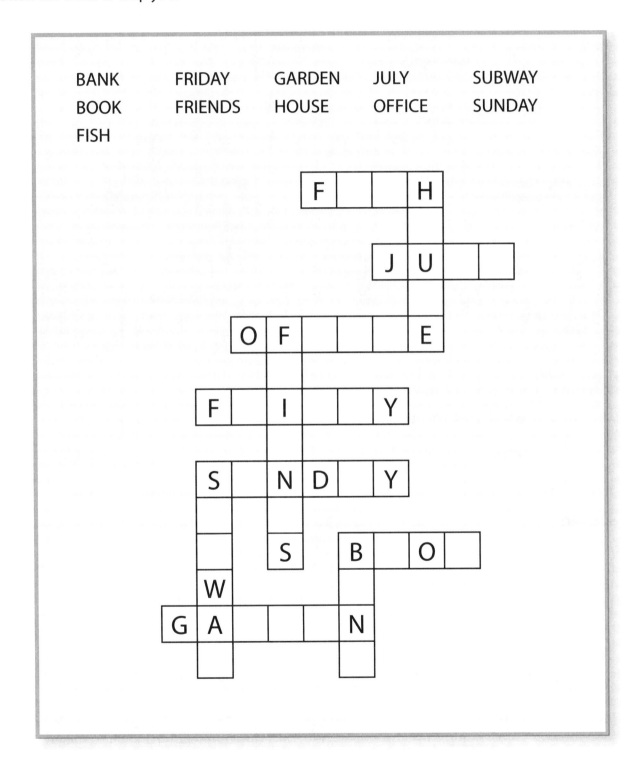

BANK   FRIDAY   GARDEN   JULY   SUBWAY

BOOK   FRIENDS   HOUSE   OFFICE   SUNDAY

FISH

Cc & Kk Vicky's Truck

Talk, Write, and Read

A. Talk about what you see in this picture.

B. Say words with the letter **c** like **car** or **k** like **key.** Do you hear the same sound? **C** and **K** often make the same sound. Sometimes the sound is spelled **c,** sometimes **k,** sometimes **ck.** Write words that have these letters.

c like **car**	k like **key**	ck like **truck**
_____	_____	_____
_____	_____	_____

Some words with **c** do not sound like **car.** Lesson 13 tells more about the letter **c.**

C. Pick two words from your list. On another sheet of paper, make a sentence using each word. Read your sentences out loud.

Notes for Unit 2: 1.A. Talk about the picture as you did in Unit 1. **B.** Follow the letter/sound lesson strategy in the TRG. Let students read their words aloud. **C.** Write the sentences that students dictate; let them copy and read them aloud.

Words to Know

car

key

truck

park

Key Words

drives	her	kids	she	work

Read and Write

A. Read the story to learn about Vicky and her truck. Write the word that fits.

Vicky's Truck

her
park
truck
work

Vicky has a new truck.

She drives her truck to _____.

She drives the _____ to her house.

She can put the truck in _____ garage.

She can drive the kids to the _____.

B. What does Vicky do with her truck? Talk about it with someone.

In Your Own Words

Would you rather drive a car or a truck? Tell about it. Your teacher will write it for you.

Notes: Do as you did in Unit 1.

Ll   At the Laundromat

Talk, Write, and Read

A. Talk about what you see in this picture.

B. Write words with the letter **l** like **laundry.**

_____   _____   _____

_____   _____   _____

_____   _____   _____

C. Pick two words from your list. Make a sentence using each word.

1. _____

_____

2. _____

_____

D. Read your sentences out loud.

Words to Know

love

laundry

clothes

children

Key Words

at	be	clean	Tuesday	will

Read and Write

A. Read to find out what Hal is doing. Write the word that fits.

At the Laundromat

clean
laundry
Tuesday
will

The Laundromat will be closed Labor Day.

On _____, the Laundromat is open.

Hal has his _____ at the Laundromat.

His clothes will be _____.

His children's clothes _____ be clean.

B. Do you do your laundry in a Laundromat? Talk about it with someone.

In Your Own Words

Tell about a chore you do for yourself or your family. Your teacher will write it for you.

Mm Ramon and Maria

Talk, Write, and Read

A. Talk about what you see in this picture.

B. Write words with the letter **m** like **man.**

_____   _____   _____

_____   _____   _____

_____   _____   _____

C. Pick two words from your list. Make a sentence using each word.

1. _____

_____

2. _____

_____

D. Read your sentences out loud.

Words to Know

man

money

woman

arm

Key Words

for	go	into	movie	pay	some	want

Read and Write

A. Read to find out what Ramon and Maria are doing. Write the word that fits.

Ramon and Maria

money
movie
pay
woman

Ramon and Maria want to go to a movie.

They get some _____ at the bank.

They _____ a man to go into the movie.

They pay a _____ for some food.

They love the _____ and the food.

B. What do Ramon and Maria do first? What do they do next? Talk about it with someone.

In Your Own Words

Tell about a movie you have enjoyed lately. Your teacher will write it for you.

Nn Stan's New Neighbor

Talk, Write, and Read

A. Talk about what you see in this picture.

B. Write words with the letter **n** like **Nancy.**

_____   _____   _____

_____   _____   _____

_____   _____   _____

C. Pick two words from your list. Make a sentence using each word.

1. _____

_____

2. _____

_____

D. Read your sentences out loud.

Words to Know

neighbor

nail

dinner

newspaper

Key Words

are	gets	next	Wednesday	with

Read and Write

A. Read the story to learn about Stan's new neighbor. Write the word that fits.

Stan's New Neighbor

dinner
gets
next
with

Nancy and Stan are new neighbors.

Nancy is Stan's _____ door neighbor.

Stan wants to have _____ with Nancy.

He _____ food on Wednesday.

Nancy has dinner _____ Stan.

B. What does Stan want? What does Nancy do? Talk about it with someone.

In Your Own Words

Tell about a neighbor who is also your friend. Your teacher will write it for you.

Pp Pat's Problem

Talk, Write, and Read

A. Talk about what you see in this picture.

B. Write words with the letter **p** like **pipe**.

_____   _____   _____

_____   _____   _____

_____   _____   _____

C. Pick two words from your list. Make a sentence using each word.

1. _____

_____

2. _____

_____

D. Read your sentences out loud.

Words to Know

pipe

plumber

happy

stop

Key Words

calls	drips	Monday	problem	so

Read and Write

A. Read the story to see what Pat does about her plumbing problem. Write the word that fits.

Pat's Problem

calls
drips
happy
pipe

Pat has a problem with a pipe.

She has a pipe that _____.

On Monday, Pat _____ a plumber.

The plumber puts in a new _____.

The drip stops, so Pat is _____.

B. What would you do if you had a plumbing problem? Talk about it with someone.

In Your Own Words

Tell about something you have had to fix at home. Your teacher will write it for you.

Qq Quinn and the Quiz Show

Talk, Write, and Read

A. Talk about what you see in this picture.

B. The letter **q** is almost always followed by the letter **u.** Write words with the letters **qu** like **quiz.**

_____   _____   _____

_____   _____   _____

C. Pick two words from your list. Make a sentence using each word.

1. _____

   _____

2. _____

   _____

D. Read your sentences out loud.

Words to Know

quarter

quiet

quart

square

Key Words

| answer | easy | likes | questions | show |

Read and Write

A. Read the story to learn what Quinn likes on TV. Write the word that fits.

Quinn and the Quiz Show

answer
easy
likes
quiz

Quinn likes the new quiz show.

She _____ to answer the questions.

Some questions are _____ for Quinn.

Quinn loves to _____ the easy questions.

Quinn is happy with her new _____ show.

B. What does Quinn like about the quiz show? Talk about it with someone.

In Your Own Words

Tell about something you like to do. Your teacher will write it for you.

Rr Rainy Morning

Talk, Write, and Read

A. Talk about what you see in this picture.

B. Write words with the letter **r** like **rain.**

_____   _____   _____

_____   _____   _____

_____   _____   _____

C. Pick two words from your list. Make a sentence using each word.

1. _____

_____

2. _____

_____

D. Read your sentences out loud.

Words to Know

radio   rainy   morning   water

Key Words

comes	it	March	must	their

Read and Write

A. Read the story to learn about Ramon and Maria's morning. Write the word that fits.

Rainy Morning

comes
must
their
water

It is a rainy morning in March.

Ramon and Maria _____ go to work.

They get up and put on _____ clothes.

Water _____ in the open window.

Ramon cleans up the _____ and they drive

to work.

B. What do Ramon and Maria do in the morning? What does he do next?

Talk about it with someone.

In Your Own Words

Tell about a time that rain spoiled your plans. Your teacher will write it for you.

Review Cc & Kk, Ll, Mm, Nn, Pp, Qq, Rr

Words to Review

Fill in the missing letter of each word. Then read the words out loud.

c	k	l	m	n	p	q	r

_____ar   _____aundry   _____ail   _____ipe

_____uarter   _____ainy   _____oney   ha_____ _____y

chi_____dren   s_____uare   wate_____   ma_____

Notes: 1. Have students read the eight consonants. Help them write the correct consonant in the first word. Let them complete the exercise as independently as possible.

Sentence Pairs

Finish these sentence pairs with the word that fits. Read the sentences out loud.

clothes
neighbors
questions

A. Hal has some laundry.

He will clean his _____.

B. Stan is next door to Nancy.

They are friends and _____.

C. Quinn likes quiz shows.

She likes to answer easy _____.

What Do You Think?

Check **YES** if you think these are good ideas. Check **NO** if they are not good ideas. Talk about the ideas with someone.

YES   NO

A. Ramon and Maria must clean the garage.

_____   _____   They go to a movie.

B. Pat has a drip in a pipe.

_____   _____   She calls a plumber.

C. Ramon must go to work.

_____   _____   He puts on his work clothes.

D. Vicky drives her truck to work.

_____   _____   She has the hood open.

Notes: 2. Have students read the sentences as independently as possible and choose the word to finish each sentence. Have them read completed sentences aloud. **3.** Help students read the sentences.

What's the Order?

A. Number the sentences in order. The first one is started for you.

1. __1__ Stan wants to have dinner with Nancy.

_____ They have dinner with Hal and Quinn.

_____ Stan calls Nancy.

2. _____ Ramon and Maria drive to a movie.

_____ They love the movie.

_____ They pay money for the movie.

B. Read the sentences in order out loud.

Writing Sentences

Make a sentence. Use all the words. Then read your sentences to someone.

must	key	truck

A. _____

children	will	love

B. _____

movie	is	quiet

C. _____

happy	to	go

D. _____

Puzzle

Read the words out loud. Write words where they fit. Use all the words. Some letters are there to help you.

ARM   HE   LOVE   PROBLEM   RADIO

CAR   HER   MONDAY   QUART   THEIR

CHILDREN   LAUNDRY   NEWSPAPER   QUIET

Cc & Ss Nancy Helps Sandy

Talk and Write

A. Talk about what you see in this picture.

B. Say words that have the letter **c** like **city** or the letter **s** like **sister.** Do you hear the same sound? **C** and **S** often make the same sound. Sometimes the sound is spelled **c;** sometimes it is spelled **s.**

C. Write words with these letters.

c like **city**	s like **sister**
_____	_____
_____	_____
_____	_____

Some words with **c** sound like **car.** We talked about them in Lesson 6.

Notes for Unit 3: 1.A. Talk about the picture as you did in Unit 1. **B.** Explain that c and s sometimes have the same sound. **C.** Follow the letter/sound lesson strategy in the TRG.

Words to Know

city

soda

sisters

pencil

Key Words

hard	help	job	June	school	study

Read and Write

A. Read the story to find why Sandy is studying. Finish the story.

Nancy Helps Sandy

Sandy is in school in the city.

She wants her GED.

She wants a new job in June.

She works hard for her GED.

Nancy and Sandy are sisters.

Nancy helps her sister study.

She helps Sandy work hard problems.

With Nancy's help, Sandy _____.

B. Why is Nancy helping Sandy study? Talk about it with someone.

In Your Own Words

Tell about someone who helps you study. Your teacher will write it.

Notes: 2. Ask students to read and talk about pictured words. **3.** Read each word; let students repeat. **4.** Discuss the purpose for reading the story. Ask students to read the story and finish the last sentence. Discuss question B. **5.** Conduct an LEA activity as before.

Tt Tony's Trip

Talk, Read, and Write

A. Talk about what you see in this picture. Read the story. Talk about the story.

Tony's Trip

In September, Tony takes a trip on the train.

He has his clothes in a suitcase.

He takes the train to the city.

Tony wants to work in the city.

B. Write words with the letter **t** like **Tony.**

_____ _____ _____

_____ _____ _____

_____ _____ _____

Notes: 1. A. Talk about the picture. Read the story aloud. Do a paired reading with students. Let students read aloud. **B.** Let students read their words aloud. They may dictate sentences with the words. Take dictation and let them copy.

Words to Know

telephone   train   suitcase   exit

Key Words

| September | takes | tells | too | trip |

Read and Write

A. Read the story to find out what Tony does in the city. Finish the story.

In the City

Tony gets a new job in the city.

He likes his new job.

He loves the city, too.

Tony calls his friend Vicky on the telephone.

He tells Vicky he likes the city.

He tells her he likes his job.

He tells Vicky _____.

B. How does Tony feel about his new life in the city? Talk about it with someone.

In Your Own Words

Tell about a trip you would like to take. Your teacher will write it.

Vv Valentine's Day

Talk, Read, and Write

A. Talk about what you see in this picture. Read the story. Talk about the story.

Valentine's Day

Tony is with Vicky on Valentine's Day, February 14.

He helps Vicky with dinner.

Vicky gives Tony a valentine.

Their dinner is very good.

B. Write words with the letter **v** like **valentine.**

_____   _____   _____

_____   _____   _____

_____   _____   _____

Words to Know

vase

valentine

television

stove

Key Words

am	dear	February	good	I	very	you

Read and Write

A. Are Vicky and Tony good friends? Read the valentine Vicky gave Tony. Finish the sentences.

Dear Tony,

Some friends are old,

Some friends are new.

I am happy to have

A good friend _____.

Some friends are new,

Some friends are old.

A dear friend like you

Is _____.

B. Do you think Vicky and Tony are good friends? Talk about it with someone.

In Your Own Words

Tell about a good friend you have. Your teacher will write it.

Ww   A Walk in the Woods

Talk, Read, and Write

A. Talk about what you see in this picture. Read the story. Talk about the story.

A Walk in the Woods

Wayne and Yo-Yo go for a walk.

They walk in the woods in October.

Yo-Yo wants to swim in the water.

Yo-Yo gets very wet.

B. Write words with the letter **w** like **water.**

_____   _____   _____

_____   _____   _____

_____   _____   _____

Words to Know

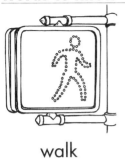

walk

woods

sidewalk

swim

Key Words

October	starts	then	wash	wet

Read and Write

A. What happens next with Wayne and Yo-Yo? Read to see what happens. Finish the story.

Wayne and Yo-Yo

Wayne wants to wash Yo-Yo.

He takes the hose.

He starts to wash Yo-Yo.

Then Yo-Yo starts to _____.

Wayne gets Yo-Yo very clean.

Then he gives Yo-Yo dinner.

For dinner, Yo-Yo gets _____.

B. What does Wayne do first? What does he do next? Talk about it with someone.

In Your Own Words

Tell about going for a walk. Your teacher will write it.

Yy Wayne's Birthday

Talk, Read, and Write

A. Talk about what you see in this picture. Read the story. Talk about the story.

Wayne's Birthday

Wayne's birthday is November 10.

Vicky and her friends have a party for Wayne.

They eat birthday cake.

They yell "Happy Birthday" to Wayne.

B. Write words with the letter **y** like **yell.**

_____   _____   _____

_____   _____   _____

_____   _____   _____

Words to Know

yell

yawn

year

yield

Key Words

birthday	cake	November	party	this

Read and Write

A. What happens on Wayne's birthday? Read the story to find out. Finish the sentences.

Wayne's Party

Wayne is happy on his birthday.

He loves the party and the cake.

He gives some cake to Yo-Yo.

Yo-Yo loves _____.

Wayne wants to have a very good year.

He tells his friends,

"This party is a very good start.

I want this year to be _____."

B. How does Wayne feel about his birthday? Talk about it with someone.

In Your Own Words

Tell a story about your birthday. Your teacher will write it.

Xx & Zz   Pizza for Dinner

Talk, Read, and Write

A. Talk about what you see in this picture. Read the story. Talk about the story.

Pizza for Dinner

Don and Pat want pizza for dinner.

They call the House of Pizza on the telephone.

They order a large pizza.

It comes in a large box.

They pay for the pizza.

B. **X** and **Z** are letters you will not use often. **X** often has an **e** in front of it, like in the word **exit.** Write words that have these letters.

 x like **exit**   **z** like **zip**

_____   _____

Words to Know

exercise

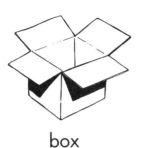

box

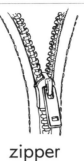

zipper

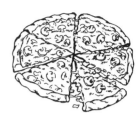

pizza

Key Words

all	feel	large	of	order

Read and Write

A. What do Don and Pat do after dinner? Read the story to find out. Finish the sentences.

Exercise

Don and Pat eat all of the large pizza.

They feel very full.

They start to yawn.

They want to _____.

Then Don and Pat get up.

They start to exercise.

They exercise hard.

This helps them _____.

B. How do Don and Pat feel after dinner? What do they do next? Talk about it with someone.

In Your Own Words

Tell about exercises you do. Your teacher will write it.

Lesson 18 **Xx & Zz** **51**

Review Cc & Ss, Tt, Vv, Ww, Yy, Xx & Zz

Words to Review

Fill in the missing letter of each word. Then read the words out loud.

c	s	t	v	w	y	x	z

____elephone

____ity

____ase

____ipper

____oods

____isters

s____im

pen____il

sui____case

tele____ision

e____ercise

side____alk

Notes: 1. Have students read the eight consonants. Let them complete the exercise as independently as possible.

Sentence Pairs

Finish these sentence pairs with the word that fits. Read the sentences out loud.

city

exercise

study

water

A. Sandy takes the subway to school.

She can _____ on the subway.

B. Tony wants a new job.

He takes a trip to the _____.

C. Yo-Yo and Wayne go for a walk.

Yo-Yo gets wet in the _____.

D. Don and Pat eat a large pizza.

Then they _____.

How Do You Know?

Read the stories out loud. Answer the questions. Read your answers.

A. Stan has a party for Nancy.

Nancy and her friends like the party.

They eat pizza and cake.

Was Stan's party a good one? How do you know?

_____

B. Vicky and Tony exercise in the morning.

Some mornings they walk in the woods.

Some mornings they swim in the water.

Do Vicky and Tony keep fit? How do you know?

_____

Notes: 2. Have students read the sentences as independently as possible and choose the word to finish each sentence. Have them read completed sentences aloud, either individually or as a group. **3.** Help students read the "How Do You Know?" stories and answer the questions. Have them read their answers aloud.

What's the Order?

A. Number the sentences in order. The first one is started for you.

1. __1__ Don and Pat want pizza for dinner.

   _____ Sandy and Nancy help them eat it.

   _____ They order a large pizza.

2. _____ Yo-Yo eats the cake.

   _____ Wayne has some birthday cake.

   _____ Wayne gives some cake to Yo-Yo.

B. Read the sentences in order out loud.

Writing Sentences

Make a sentence. Use all the words. Then read your sentences to someone.

study	year	school

A. _____

give	valentine	friend

B. _____

trip	clothes	suitcase

C. _____

take	walk	woods

D. _____

Notes: 4. Discuss the meaning of sequence. Let students complete the exercise as independently as possible.
5. Have students copy their sentences and read them aloud.

Puzzle

Read the words out loud. Write words where they fit. Use all the words. Some letters are there to help you.

BOX   FEBRUARY   SCHOOL   STOVE   TRAIN

CALL   PENCIL   SEPTEMBER   TELEPHONE   VASE

CITY   PIZZA   SIDEWALK   TELEVISION   YEAR

EXIT

Aa   Short a

Talk and Read

Talk about what you see in this picture. Listen to the limerick. Read it. Talk about how it sounds.

Nancy's New Cat

A good friend of Nancy's is Pat.

Pat gives her a fat tabby cat.

The cat eats some ham,

And crab apple jam,

Then it naps on Nancy's new hat.

Word Families

Read the words in these families. Write one more word in each family. Write any words you know.

-at	-am	-ap	-ab
hat	ham	cap	cab
sat	ram	nap	nab
flat	cram	trap	crab
___	___	___	___

Notes for Unit 4: 1. Talk about the picture. Talk about rhyme and about limericks (see TRG); read the limerick. **2.** Explain word families (see TRG). Have students read the words aloud and add another word to each family.

a b c d e f g h i j k l m n o p q r s t u v w x y z

Words to Know

apple	back	makes	not	quite

Read and Write

Read the sentences. Write the word that fits.

Nancy's Hat

cab
flat
happy
nap
Pat

Nancy has a new hat.

The cat takes a _____ on Nancy's

new hat.

This makes the hat quite _____.

Nancy is not _____.

She calls Hal in his _____.

Hal drives the cat back to _____.

Writing Sentences

Write sentences. Use both words. Then read your sentences out loud to someone.

sat	cab

A. _____

cat	nap

B. _____

In Your Own Words

Tell about a pet you know. Your teacher will write it.

Notes: 3. Read the words aloud; have students repeat. **4.** Have students read the sentences, filling in blanks with the appropriate word. **5.** Have students dictate and copy, or write sentences on their own. Have them read their sentences aloud. **6.** Conduct an LEA activity.

Ee Short e

Talk and Read

Talk about what you see in this picture. Listen to the limerick. Read it. Talk about how it sounds.

Sandy Learns to Spell

Sandy is learning to spell.

She writes **sell** when she wants to write **cell.**

Oh, it is quite a mess

When **c** sounds like **s**

But soon she will spell very well.

Word Families

Read the words in these families. Write one more word in each family. Write any words you know.

-ed	-ell	-ess	-et
led	tell	less	get
red	yell	mess	wet
shed	spell	dress	yet
___	___	___	___

Words to Know

learning	soon	sounds	when	writes

Read and Write

Read the sentences. Write the word that fits.

A Job with a Vet

beds
fed
gets
when

Ted is a vet.

In May, Sandy _____ a job with Ted.

She cleans the pets' messy _____.

She gets the pets _____.

She tells Ted _____ the pets are not well.

Writing Sentences

Write sentences. Use both words. Then read your sentences out loud to someone.

sell	dress

A. _____

shed	pet

B. _____

In Your Own Words

Tell about a job that you do. Your teacher will write it for you.

Ii   Short i

Talk and Read

Talk about what you see in this picture. Listen to the limerick. Read it. Talk about how it sounds.

Vicky Cooks Fish

Vicky cooks fish on the grill.

And all of her friends eat their fill.

Vicky's friends all just sit.

They do not help a bit,

Until Vicky writes them a bill.

Word Families

Read the words in these families. Write one more word in each family. Write any words you know.

-ick	-ill	-ip	-it
kick	fill	dip	bit
pick	hill	zip	sit
quick	grill	chip	quit
_____	_____	_____	_____

Words to Know

as	cooks	do	just	until

Read and Write

Read the sentences. Write the word that fits.

Dinner at Vicky's

dinner
dip
grill
sit

Vicky picks up the fish.

She fills the _____ with fish.

Her friends just _____ as she cooks.

They eat chips and _____.

They all eat fish for _____.

Writing Sentences

Write sentences. Use both words. Then read your sentences out loud to someone.

tickets	trip

A. _____

flip	grill

B. _____

In Your Own Words

Tell about a picnic you have been to. Your teacher will write it for you.

Oo Short o

Talk and Read

Talk about what you see in this picture. Listen to the limerick. Read it. Talk about
how it sounds.

A Jog in the Fog

Don takes his dog for a jog

On a day with a very thick fog.

They jog down the block,

And Don hits a rock.

Now Don does not jog in the fog.

Word Families

Read the words in these families. Write one more word in each family. Write any
words you know.

-ob	-ock	-og	-op
cob	mock	fog	cop
job	rock	log	mop
rob	block	frog	stop
___	___	___	___

Words to Know

does	down	now	Saturday

Read and Write

Read the sentences. Write the word that fits.

Don and His Dog

block

dog

stop

top

On Saturday, Don jogs with his dog.

They jog down the _____.

They jog to the _____ of the hill.

They _____ when they get to the top.

The _____ is happy when they stop.

Writing Sentences

Write sentences. Use both words. Then read your sentences out loud to someone.

down	rock

A. _____

job	top

B. _____

In Your Own Words

Tell how you feel about jogging. Your teacher will write it for you.

Uu Short u

Talk and Read

Talk about what you see in this picture. Listen to the limerick. Read it. Talk about how it sounds.

Gus's Lunch

For lunch my friend Gus eats a sub.

On some days he will eat a club.

With a tug on the plug

Of his cold water jug

Gus washes down all his good grub.

Word Families

Read the words in these families. Write one more word in each family. Write any words you know.

-ub	-uff	-ug	-un
rub	cuff	bug	bun
tub	puff	hug	fun
grub	scuff	plug	run
_____	_____	_____	_____

Words to Know

cold	January	lunch	my	push

Read and Write

Read the sentences. Write the word that fits.

Lunch in the Sun

fun
push
sun
truck

It is a cold, sunny day in January.

Gus wants to eat lunch in the _____.

He drives his _____ to the bluff.

He has _____ until the truck gets stuck.

Gus must get Vicky to _____ with

her truck.

Writing Sentences

Write sentences. Use both words. Then read your sentences out loud to someone.

rug	stuff

A. _____

tub	run

B. _____

In Your Own Words

Tell what you like for lunch. Your teacher will write it for you.

Review Short a e i o u

Sentence Pairs

Finish the sentence pairs. Write the word that fits. Then read the sentences out loud.

cold	down	lunch	until
cooks	learning	make	writes

A. 1. Sandy is _____ to spell.

2. She _____ to her friend Wayne.

B. 1. Vicky _____ fish on the grill.

2. Her friends eat _____ they are full.

C. 1. Don jogs _____ the block.

2. He does not get _____ when he jogs.

D. 1. Gus makes a sub for _____.

2. Now and then he may _____ a club.

Notes: 1. Let students read and complete the exercise as independently as possible. Have them read each sentence pair aloud as they complete it, checking the meaning of the sentences as they do.

Word Families

Write one word that belongs in each family.

-at hat	**-am** ham	**-ap** cap	**-ab** cab
_____	_____	_____	_____
-ed bed	**-ell** fell	**-ess** mess	**-et** let
_____	_____	_____	_____
-ick sick	**-ill** fill	**-ip** dip	**-it** pit
_____	_____	_____	_____
-ob sob	**-ock** dock	**-og** bog	**-op** cop
_____	_____	_____	_____
-ub tub	**-uff** muff	**-ug** hug	**-un** run
_____	_____	_____	_____

Notes: 2. Have students complete the word families on their own. Have them read each family aloud to check the appropriateness of the words they've written.

Make Words

Put the letter with the word families to make words. Read the words.

A. l   ____ab   ____et   ____ip   ____og   ____ug

B. p   ____at   ____et   ____it   ____ot   ____uff

C. t   ____ab   ____ell   ____ick   ____op   ____ug

D. s   ____at   ____ell   ____ick   ____ock   ____un

E. b   ____at   ____et   ____ill   ____og   ____ug

What Do You Want to Do?

Check what you would like to do. Tell why.

____ Jog down the block.   ____ Eat a sub for lunch.

____ Eat fish from the grill.   ____ Learn to spell.

____ Get a cat for a pet.   ____ Work for a vet.

Writing Sentences

Write sentences. Use all the words. Read your sentences.

pick	red	apple

A. _____

fill	jug	Pat

B. _____

run	tell	mess

C. _____

Notes: 3. Have students read the words they form. **4.** Have students read the choices and check the ones they would enjoy. Have them explain their reasoning. **5.** Take dictation or let students write sentences on their own.

Puzzle

Read the words out loud. Write words where they fit. Use all the words. Some letters are there to help you.

APPLE   DRESS   JANUARY   PUSH   SOUNDS

AT   GARDEN   LEARNING   QUICK   SPELL

DINNER   GRILL   NAP   ROCK   STOP

DOES   HAPPY   PAN   RUN   THEIR

DOWN   HIS   PLUG   SATURDAY   WRITE

B & C   Blends bl br cl cr

Talk and Read

Talk about what you see in this picture. Read Quinn's rules. Why does Quinn need these rules?

Quinn's Rules

1. Clean up clutter.

2. Put clothes in the closet.

3. Brush up crumbs.

4. Sweep the house with a broom.

5. Blot up drinks you spill.

Blends

Read the words. Write one more word with each blend.

bl	br	cl	cr
blot	bring	closet	crock
bless	broom	club	crop
bluff	brush	clutter	crumb
_____	_____	_____	_____

Notes for Unit 5: 1. Talk about the picture as before. Read the selection. Let students repeat. **2.** Read words with blends with students. Have students find words with blends from the reading. Let students add words of their own.

Make Words

Put the blends with the word families to make words.

bl	br	cl	cr

_____ab   _____am   _____ick   _____ock

_____ab   _____am   _____ick   _____ock

Words to Know

keeps	pick	rules	spill	sweep

Read and Think

Read the story. Answer the questions after the story.

Quinn keeps her house clean. The children help her. They sweep up crumbs. They pick up clutter. They put their clothes in the closet. Quinn likes a clean house.

A. Pick the better title. Write it above the story.

_____ (1) Quinn's House

_____ (2) Quinn's Job

B. What do the children do with clutter?

_____ (1) pick it up

_____ (2) sweep it up

C. What can you tell about Quinn's children?

_____ (1) They help with the housework.

_____ (2) They like to run.

In Your Own Words

Tell about the rules you would write for people in your home. Your teacher will write it for you.

Notes: 3. Demonstrate how to match blends and word families to make words. Have students read the words. **4.** Read the words aloud; have students repeat. **5.** Read the story: let students repeat. Read each question and let students choose the correct answer. **6.** Conduct an LEA activity.

Lesson 24 **B & C Blends** 71

D & F   Blends dr fl fr

Talk and Read

Talk about what you see in this picture. Read this story to find out about Frank's problem.

Frank's Problem

Frank works for a flower shop. He drives the truck.

Frank puts fresh flowers on the floor of the truck.

When Frank drives, the flowers flip over.

Flowers drop on the floor and break.

Blends

Read the words with these blends. Write one more word with each blend.

dr	**fl**	**fr**
drag	flip	Frank
drip	floor	fresh
drop	flower	friend
_____	_____	_____

Make Words

Put the blends with the word families to make words.

dr	fl	fr

| ___ag | ___esh | ___ip | ___op |
| ___ag | ___esh | ___ip | ___op |

Words to Know

break	holds	over	plan	shop

Read and Think

Read the story. Answer the questions after the story.

Frank has a plan. He drags a large box to the truck. He nails it to the floor. The box holds the flowers. Now the flowers do not flip over. Now they do not drop and break.

A. Pick the better title. Write it above the story.

_____ (1) Flowers in the Truck

_____ (2) Frank's Plan

B. What was Frank's plan?

_____ (1) nail a box to the floor to hold the flowers

_____ (2) put the flowers on the floor of the truck

C. What do you think of Frank's plan? Talk about it with someone.

In Your Own Words

Tell about how you have solved a problem. Your teacher will write it for you.

G & P Blends gl gr pl pr

Talk and Read

Talk about what you see in this picture. Read about Sandy's hopes
for the future.

Graduation

In April, Sandy gets her GED diploma. Her family comes to
the program. Her friends come, too. Her family and friends
are happy for her. Sandy is glad they are proud. Now she
plans to find a better job.

Blends

Read the words with beginning blends. Write one more word with each blend.

gl	gr	pl	pr
glad	graduation	plan	press
glass	grand	plug	program
gloom	grill	plumber	proud
_____	_____	_____	_____

Make Words

Put the blends with the word families to make words.

gl	gr	pl	pr

_____ ass   _____ and   _____ op   _____ um

_____ ass   _____ and   _____ op   _____ um

Words to Know

applies	April	better	diploma	find

Read and Think

Read the story. Answer the questions after the story.

Sandy has her GED. Now she wants a better job. She applies for a job at Grand Press. She gets the job! She is proud. She is glad she has her GED. She is glad she works at Grand Press.

A. Pick the better title. Write it above the story.

_____ (1) A Better Job

_____ (2) Sandy Gets Her GED

B. What helped Sandy get her new job?

_____ (1) She has her GED.

_____ (2) She is proud.

C. What can you tell about Sandy?

_____ (1) She likes to have fun.

_____ (2) She wants to work.

In Your Own Words

Tell about the benefits of having a GED. Your teacher will write it for you.

S   Blends sl sm sp st

Talk and Read

Talk about what you see in this picture. Read the story. What do you think will happen next?

Stan's Spaghetti Sauce

On Thursday, Stan makes spaghetti sauce in a pot. He stirs the sauce. The sauce smells good as it steams. Stan puts the top on the pot. Then he takes a nap.

Blends

Read the words with beginning blends. Write one more word with each blend.

sl	sm	sp	st
slap	smell	spaghetti	steam
sleep	smog	spell	stick
slope	smoke	spill	stove
_____	_____	_____	_____

Make Words

Put the blends with the word families to make words.

sl	sm	sp	st
____ell	____ill	____ick	____op
____ell	____ill	____ick	____op

Words to Know

off	sauce	stir	Thursday	today	turns

Read and Think

Read the story. Answer the questions after the story.

Stan sleeps. The sauce spills over the pot. It sticks to the stove. Then it starts to smoke. Soon Stan smells the smoke.

Stan gets up and turns off the stove. He slaps at the smoke. He cleans up the spill. Stan is not happy. He will not have spaghetti today!

A. Pick the better title. Write it above the story.

_____ (1) Up in Smoke

_____ (2) Spaghetti for Dinner

B. What do you think Stan learned from this mess?

_____ (1) not to sleep when he cooks

_____ (2) not to clean house when he cooks

In Your Own Words

Tell about a silly mistake you have made. Your teacher will write it for you.

S & T Blends sk sn tr tw

Talk and Read

Talk about what you see in this picture. Read the story. What do Ramon and Maria want to do?

Ramon and Maria

Ramon is twenty-five. Maria is twenty-two. They want to see snow. Ramon wants to learn to ski. Maria wants to learn to skate. In February, they take a trip to Twin Tree Hill.

Blends

Read the words with beginning blends. Write one more word with each blend.

sk	sn	tr	tw
skate	snap	train	twenty
ski	snip	tree	twice
skid	snow	try	twin
_____	_____	_____	_____

Make Words

Put the blends with the word families to make words.

sk	sn	tr	tw

| _____ack | _____im | _____in | _____uck |
| _____ack | _____im | _____in | _____uck |

Words to Know

again	past	see	tries	well

Read and Think

Read the story. Answer the questions after the story.

Ramon is learning to ski. He can ski down the easy slope. He tries the hard slope and skids past a tree. Ramon sticks to the easy slope.

Maria learns to skate. She slips and falls. She gets up and tries again. She learns to skate very well.

A. Pick the better title. Write it above the story.

_____ (1) Learning to Ski and Skate

_____ (2) The Easy Slope

B. What can you tell about Ramon and Maria?

_____ (1) They do not get cold.

_____ (2) They do not give up.

In Your Own Words

Tell about a skill or sport you would like to try. Your teacher will write it for you.

Review Blends beginning with B, C, D, F, G, P, S, T

Sentence Pairs

Finish the sentence pairs. Write the word that fits.

better	comes	keep	sauce
break	finds	rules	turns

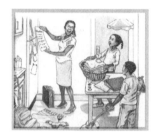

A. 1. Quinn tries to _____ her house clean.

2. She has _____ for her children.

B. 1. The flowers _____ when Frank drives.

2. Frank _____ a box to hold the flowers.

C. 1. Sandy's family _____ to her graduation.

2. They want her to get a _____ job.

D. 1. Stan wants to make spaghetti _____ today.

2. He _____ on the stove to cook the sauce.

Notes: 1. Let students read and complete the exercise as independently as possible. Have them read each sentence pair aloud as they complete it, checking the meaning of the sentences as they do.

Make Words

Put blends with word families to make words. Read the words.

A.

dr	sp	gr	pl
_____ab ·	_____an	_____ip	_____um
_____ab	_____an	_____ip	_____um

B.

cl	st	sk	fr
_____ill	_____ip	_____ock	_____ump
_____ill	_____ip	_____ock	_____ump

C.

fl	tr	sm	cr
_____ap	_____ick	_____ock	_____ush
_____ap	_____ick	_____ock	_____ush

D.

br	pr	sl	sn
_____ag	_____op	_____ug	_____ush
_____ag	_____op	_____ug	_____ush

What Do You Want to Do?

Check the activities that you want to do. Tell why.

_____ Ski down a hill.

_____ Drive a truck.

_____ Get some fresh flowers.

_____ Clean up the house.

_____ Take a trip.

_____ Cook some spaghetti.

Notes: 2. Let students work independently. Have them read each word aloud to be sure it is actually a word.
3. Have students read the list and check off what they'd like to do.

How Do You Know?

Read the stories out loud. Answer the questions. Read your answers.

A. Sandy wants to help her friend Wayne get his GED. She tells him she will help him study. She tells him he can get a better job.

Does Sandy plan to help Wayne? How do you know?

_____

B. Ramon and Maria like to go to movies. They like to give birthday parties for their friends. They love to take trips.

Do Ramon and Maria like to have fun? How do you know?

_____

Writing Sentences

Write sentences. Use all the words. Read your sentences.

drop	crumbs	floor

A. _____

like	skate	ski

B. _____

smell	flowers	fresh

C. _____

glad	stove	clean

D. _____

Notes: 4. Let students read the stories and questions. Let them write the answers on their own. Discuss their answers.
5. Take dictation or let students write sentences on their own.

Puzzle

Read the words out loud. Write words where they fit. Use all the words. Some letters are there to help you.

BLESS   DIG   FRIEND   RULE   STICK

BLOT   DIPLOMA   GLAD   RUN   THURSDAY

BRUSH   DRAG   GLASS   SKID   TREE

CAR   DROP   GRADUATION   SOON   TRY

CLOTHES   FLIP   OLD   SPAGHETTI   TWICE

CROCK   FLOORS

Answer Key

Unit 1

Lesson 1: Bb

Read and Write (p. 7)

The **book** is open.

The book is **closed.**

The book **is** closed.

The **bank** is closed.

The bookstore is **open.**

The bank **is** closed Sunday.

The bookstore is open Sunday.

Lesson 2: Dd

Read and Write (p. 9)

Don's office **has** a door.

Don has a **desk.**

The desk is **full.**

Don's **office** has a window.

The window has **a** shade.

The **window** is closed in December.

Lesson 3: Ff

Read and Write (p. 11)

Frank and his friends eat **fish** on Friday.

Frank and his **friends** eat french fries.

Frank and his friends drink **coffee.**

Frank eats half his fish **and** french fries.

Frank is **full.**

His friends eat his **food.**

Lesson 4: Hh

Read and Write (p. 13)

Hal has the **hood** open.

The hose is **old.**

The hose has a **hole.**

Hal has a new hose in his **hand.**

He **puts** the new hose in the cab.

Hal closes the hood.

Lesson 5: Gg & Jj

Read and Write (p. 15)

They **dig** up the garden in May.

They **grow** food in the garden.

They grow food for their friends.

Read and Write (p. 17)

They **put** the vegetables in a wagon.

They put the **wagon** in the garage.

They close the **garden** gate.

Jan and Gus **can** eat the vegetables.

They **give** them to friends in July and August.

They give **vegetables** to Frank and Hal.

Unit 1 Review

Words to Review (p. 18)

door, July, **g**arden, **d**esk

fish, **g**ate, **h**and, win**d**ow

book, co**ff**ee, di**g**, hal**f**

Sentence Pairs (p. 19)

A. December   C. vegetables

B. coffee   D. hose

How Do You Know? (p. 19)

A. 2   B. 1   C. 1   D. 2

What's the Order? (p. 20)

A. 1. <u>1</u> Hal has an old hose in his cab.

   <u>3</u> Hal puts in a new hose.

   <u>2</u> Hal opens the hood.

   2. <u>2</u> Jan and Gus dig up the vegetables.

   <u>1</u> Vegetables grow in the garden.

   <u>3</u> Jan and Gus give vegetables to friends.

Writing Sentences (p. 20)

Sentences will vary.

Puzzle (p. 21)

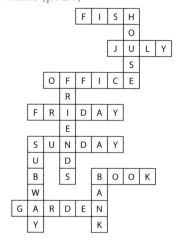

Unit 2

Lesson 6: Cc & Kk

Read and Write (p. 23)

A. She drives her truck to **work.**

She drives the **truck** to her house.

She can put the truck in **her** garage.

She can drive the kids to the **park.**

Lesson 7: Ll

Read and Write (p. 25)

A. On **Tuesday,** the Laundromat is open.

Hal has his **laundry** at the Laundromat.

His clothes will be **clean.**

His children's clothes **will** be clean.

Lesson 8: Mm

Read and Write (p. 27)

A. They get some **money** at the bank.

They **pay** a man to go into the movie.

They pay a **woman** for some food.

They love the **movie** and the food.

Lesson 9: Nn

Read and Write (p. 29)

A. Nancy is Stan's **next** door neighbor.

Stan wants to have **dinner** with Nancy.

He **gets** food on Wednesday.

Nancy has dinner **with** Stan.

Lesson 10: Pp

Read and Write (p. 31)

A. She has a pipe that **drips.**

On Monday, Pat **calls** a plumber.

The plumber puts in a new **pipe.**

The drip stops, so Pat is **happy.**

Lesson 11: Qq

Read and Write (p. 33)

A. She **likes** to answer the questions.

Some questions are **easy** for Quinn.

Quinn loves to **answer** the easy questions.

Quinn is happy with her new **quiz** show.

Lesson 12: Rr

Read and Write (p. 35)

A. Ramon and Maria **must** go to work.

They get up and put on **their** clothes.

Water **comes** in the open window.

Ramon cleans up the **water** and they drive to work.

Unit 2 Review

Words to Review (p. 36)

car, **l**aundry, **n**ail, **p**ipe

quarter, **r**ainy, **m**oney, ha**pp**y

children, **s**quare, **w**ater, ma**n**

Sentence Pairs (p. 37)

A. clothes   B. neighbors   C. questions

What Do You Think? (p. 37)

Answers will vary.

What's the Order? (p. 38)

A. 1. 1 Stan wants to have dinner with Nancy.

   3 They have dinner with Hal and Quinn.

   2 Stan calls Nancy.

2. 1 Ramon and Maria drive to a movie.

   3 They love the movie.

   2 They pay money for the movie.

Writing Sentences (p. 38)

Sentences will vary.

Puzzle (p. 39)

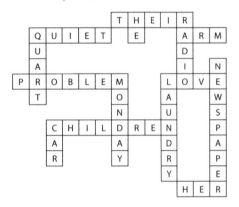

Unit 3

Lessons 13–18

Read and Write (pp. 41, 43, 45, 47, 49, 51)

Sentence completions will vary.

Unit 3 Review

Words to Review (p. 52)

telephone, **c**ity, **v**ase, **z**ipper

woods, **s**isters, **s**wim, pen**c**il

suitcase, television, e**x**ercise, side**w**alk

Sentence Pairs (p. 53)

A. study   B. city   C. water   D. exercise

How Do You Know? (p. 53)

A. We know his party is a good one because Nancy and her friends all like the party.

B. We know Vicky and Tony keep fit because they swim or walk in the morning.

What's the Order? (p. 54)

A. 1. 1 Don and Pat want pizza for dinner.

<u>3</u> Sandy and Nancy help them eat it.

<u>2</u> They order a large pizza.

2. <u>3</u> Yo-Yo eats the cake.

<u>1</u> Wayne has some birthday cake.

<u>2</u> Wayne gives some cake to Yo-Yo.

Writing Sentences (p. 54)
Sentences will vary.

Puzzle (p. 55)

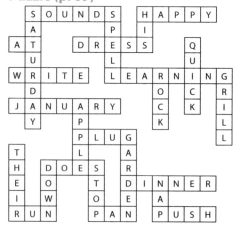

Unit 4

Lesson 19: Aa

Read and Write (p. 57)
The cat takes a **nap** on Nancy's new hat.

This makes the hat quite **flat.**

Nancy is not **happy.**

She calls Hal in his **cab.**

Hal drives the cat back to **Pat.**

Lesson 20: Ee

Read and Write (p. 59)
In May, Sandy **gets** a job with Ted.

She cleans the pets' messy **beds.**

She gets the pets **fed.**

She tells Ted **when** the pets are not well.

Lesson 21: Ii

Read and Write (p. 61)
She fills the **grill** with fish.

Her friends just **sit** as she cooks.

They eat chips and **dip.**

They all eat fish for **dinner.**

Lesson 22: Oo

Read and Write (p. 63)
They jog down the **block.**

They jog to the **top** of the hill.

They **stop** when they get to the top.

The **dog** is happy when they stop.

Lesson 23: Uu

Read and Write (p. 65)
Gus wants to eat lunch in the **sun.**

He drives his **truck** to the bluff.

He has **fun** until the truck gets stuck.

Gus must get Vicky to **push** with her truck.

Unit 4 Review

Sentence Pairs (p. 66)
A. 1. learning   2. writes

B. 1. cooks   2. until

C. 1. down   2. cold

D. 1. lunch   2. make

Word Families (p. 67)
Additional words will vary.

Make Words (p. 68)
A. lab, let, lip, log, lug

B. pat, pet, pit, pot, puff

C. tab, tell, tick, top, tug

D. sat, sell, sick, sock, sun

E. bat, bet, bill, bog, bug

What Do You Want to Do? (p. 68)
Answers will vary.

Writing Sentences (p. 68)
Sentences will vary.

Puzzle (p. 69)

Unit 5

Lesson 24: B & C Blends

Make Words (p. 71)
blab, crab

clam, cram

brick, click, crick

block, clock, crock

Read and Think (p. 71)

A. (1) Quinn's House

B. (1) pick it up

C. (1) They help with the housework.

Lesson 25: D & F Blends

Make Words (p. 73)

drag, flag

flesh, fresh

drip, flip

drop, flop

Read and Think (p. 73)

A. (2) Frank's Plan

B. (1) nail a box to the floor to hold the flowers

C. Answers will vary.

Lesson 26: G & P Blends

Make Words (p. 75)

glass, grass

gland, grand

glop, plop, prop

glum, plum

Read and Think (p. 75)

A. (1) A Better Job

B. (1) She has her GED.

C. (2) She wants to work.

Lesson 27: S Blends

Make Words (p. 77)

smell, spell

spill, still

slick, stick

slop, stop

Read and Think (p. 77)

A. (1) Up in Smoke

B. (1) not to sleep when he cooks

Lesson 28: S & T Blends

Make Words (p. 79)

snack, track

skim, trim

skin, twin

snuck, truck

Read and Think (p. 79)

A. (1) Learning to Ski and Skate

B. (2) They do not give up.

Unit 5 Review

Sentence Pairs (p. 80)

A. 1. keep   2. rules

B. 1. break   2. finds

C. 1. comes   2. better

D. 1. sauce   2. turns

Make Words (p. 81)

A. drab, grab   C. flap, trap

   span, plan   flick, trick, crick

   drip, grip   flock, smock, crock

   drum, plum   flush, crush

B. still, skill, frill   D. brag, slag, snag

   clip, skip   prop, slop

   clock, stock, frock   slug, snug

   clump, stump, frump   brush, slush

What Do You Want to Do? (p. 81)

Answers will vary.

How Do You Know? (p. 82)

A. Sandy plans to help Wayne. She tells him she will help him study.

B. Ramon and Maria like to have fun. They like to go to the movies, to have parties, and to take trips.

Writing Sentences (p. 82)

Sentences will vary.

Puzzle (p. 83)

Numbers

1	**one**	15	**fifteen**
2	**two**	16	**sixteen**
3	**three**	17	**seventeen**
4	**four**	18	**eighteen**
5	**five**	19	**nineteen**
6	**six**	20	**twenty**
7	**seven**	30	**thirty**
8	**eight**	40	**forty**
9	**nine**	50	**fifty**
10	**ten**	60	**sixty**
11	**eleven**	70	**seventy**
12	**twelve**	80	**eighty**
13	**thirteen**	90	**ninety**
14	**fourteen**	100	**one hundred**

Months of the Year

January	Jan.		**July**	Jul.
February	Feb.		**August**	Aug.
March	Mar.		**September**	Sept.
April	Apr.		**October**	Oct.
May	May		**November**	Nov.
June	Jun.		**December**	Dec.

Days of the Week

Sunday Monday Tuesday Wednesday Thursday Friday Saturday

Sunday	Sun.		**Thursday**	Thurs.
Monday	Mon.		**Friday**	Fri.
Tuesday	Tues.		**Saturday**	Sat.
Wednesday	Wed.			

Word List

Word	Lesson	Word	Lesson
a	2	cab	1
again	28	cake	17
all	18	call	10
am	15	can	5
an	2	cap	19
and	3	car	6
answer	11	cat	19
apple	19	cell	20
applies	26	children	7
April	26	chip	21
are	9	city	13
arm	8	clean	7
as	21	closed	1
at	7	closet	24
August	5	clothes	7
back	19	club	23
bank	1	clutter	24
be	7	cob	22
bed	20	coffee	3
better	26	cold	23
bill	21	comes	12
birthday	17	cooks	21
bit	21	cop	22
bless	24	crab	19
block	22	cram	19
blot	24	crock	24
bluff	23	crop	24
book	1	crumb	24
bookstore	1	cuff	23
box	18	day	7
break	25	dear	15
bring	24	December	2
broom	24	desk	2
brush	24	dig	5
bug	23	dinner	9
bun	23	dip	21
but	20	diploma	26

Word	Lesson	Word	Lesson
do	21	garage	5
does	22	garden	5
dog	22	gate	5
Don	2	GED	13
door	2	get	9
down	22	giant	5
drag	25	give	5
dress	20	glad	26
drink	3	glass	26
drip	10	gloom	26
drive	6	go	8
drop	25	good	15
easy	11	graduation	26
eat	3	grand	26
exercise	18	grill	21
exit	14	grow	5
family	26	grub	23
fast	3	Gus	5
fat	19	Hal	4
February	15	half	3
fed	20	ham	19
feel	18	hand	4
fill	21	happy	10
find	26	hard	13
fish	3	has	2
flat	19	hat	19
flip	21	have	5
floor	25	he	4
flower	25	help	13
fog	22	her	6
food	3	hill	21
for	8	his	3
Frank	3	hit	22
french fries	3	holds	25
fresh	25	hole	4
Friday	3	hood	4
friend	3	hose	4
frog	22	house	4
full	2	hug	23
fun	23	I	15

Word	Lesson	Word	Lesson
in	2	movie	8
into	8	must	12
is	1	my	23
it	12	nab	19
jacket	5	nail	9
jam	19	Nancy	9
Jan	5	nap	19
January	23	neighbor	9
job	13	new	4
jog	22	newspaper	9
jug	23	next	9
June	13	not	19
July	5	November	17
just	21	now	22
keeps	24	October	16
key	6	of	18
kick	21	off	27
kid	6	office	2
labor	7	old	4
large	18	on	3
Laundromat	7	open	1
laundry	7	order	18
learning	20	over	25
led	20	park	6
less	20	party	17
like	11	past	28
log	22	Pat	10
love	7	pay	8
lunch	23	pencil	13
makes	19	pet	20
man	8	pick	21
March	12	pipe	10
Maria	8	pizza	18
May	5	plan	25
mess	20	plug	23
mock	22	plumber	10
Monday	10	pot	27
money	8	press	26
mop	22	problem	10
morning	12	program	26

Word	Lesson		Word	Lesson
proud	26		sit	21
puff	23		skate	28
push	23		ski	28
put	4		skid	28
quart	11		slap	27
quarter	11		sleep	27
question	11		slope	27
quick	21		smell	27
quiet	11		smog	27
Quinn	11		smoke	27
quit	21		snap	28
quite	19		snip	28
quiz	11		snow	28
radio	12		so	10
rainy	12		soda	13
ram	19		some	8
Ramon	8		soon	20
red	20		sounds	20
rob	22		spaghetti	27
rock	22		spell	20
rub	23		spill	24
rug	23		square	11
rules	24		Stan	9
run	23		starts	16
Sandy	13		steam	27
sat	19		stick	27
Saturday	22		stir	27
sauce	27		stop	10
school	13		stove	15
scuff	23		stuck	23
see	28		study	13
sell	20		stuff	23
September	14		sub	23
shade	2		subway	1
she	6		suitcase	14
shed	20		sun	23
shop	25		Sunday	1
show	11		sweep	24
sidewalk	16		swim	16
sister	13		tabby	19

Word	Lesson	Word	Lesson
takes	14	up	5
Ted	20	valentine	15
telephone	14	vase	15
television	15	vegetables	5
tell	14	vet	20
the	1	very	15
their	12	Vicky	6
them	5	wagon	5
then	16	walk	16
they	5	want	8
this	17	wash	16
Thursday	27	water	12
ticket	21	Wayne	16
to	5	Wednesday	9
today	27	well	20
Tony	14	wet	16
too	14	when	20
top	22	will	7
train	14	window	2
trap	19	with	9
tree	28	woman	8
tries	28	woods	16
trip	14	work	6
truck	6	writes	20
try	28	yawn	17
tub	23	year	17
Tuesday	7	yell	17
tug	23	yet	20
turns	27	yield	17
twenty	28	you	15
twice	28	Yo-Yo	16
twin	28	zip	21
until	21	zipper	18